HMH

Teacher Edition – Book 14

Unit 5   Geometry (continued)

Module 16   Fraction Foundations

Common Core State Standards © Copyright 2010. National Governors Association Center for Best Practices and Council of Chief State School Officers. All rights reserved.

This product is not sponsored or endorsed by the Common Core State Standards Initiative of the National Governors Association Center for Best Practices and the Council of Chief State School Officers.

Excerpt from *Principles for the Design of Mathematics Curricula: Promoting Language and Content Development* by Jeff Zwiers, Jack Dieckmann, Sara Rutherford-Quach, Vinci Daro, Renae Skarin, Steven Weiss, and James Malamut. Stanford University Center for Assessment, Learning and Equity. Reprinted by permission of Stanford University Center for Assessment, Learning and Equity.

Currency and Coins Photos Courtesy of United States Mint, Bureau of Engraving and Houghton Mifflin Harcourt

Printed in the U.S.A.

ISBN 978-0-358-13208-0

3 4 5 6 7 8 9 10   0877   28 27 26 25 24 23 22 21

4500820924   C D E F G

FRACTION FOUNDATIONS

Introduce and Check for Readiness
• Module Opener   • Are You Ready?

Lesson 1—1 Day
Build Understanding

Take Apart Two-Dimensional Shapes
Learning Objective: Show same-size shapes within a circle or rectangle.
Review Vocabulary: circle, square

Lesson 2—1 Day
Connect Concepts
and Skills

Identify Equal or Unequal Shares
Learning Objective: Identify equal or unequal shares in a circle or rectangle.
New Vocabulary: equal shares, unequal shares

Lesson 3—1 Day
Connect Concepts
and Skills

Partition Shapes into Halves
Learning Objective: Separate circles and rectangles into halves
and describe the whole as two of the shares.
Online Professional Learning Video
New Vocabulary: halves, half of

Lesson 4—1 Day
Connect Concepts
and Skills

Partition Shapes into Fourths
Learning Objective: Separate circles and rectangles into fourths
and describe the whole as four of the shares.
New Vocabulary: fourths, fourth of, quarters, quarter of

Assessment
• Module 16 Test (Forms A and B)
• Unit 5 Performance Task after Module 16

See the entire scope and sequence in the Planning and Pacing Guide.

Build Understanding   Connect Concepts and Skills   Apply and Practice

TEACHING FOR DEPTH: Fraction Foundations

Make Connections Before Grade 1, children used their knowledge of shapes to analyze and compare shapes, including attributes such as number of sides and number of corners or vertices. Children also made new shapes by composing smaller shapes into larger shapes.

In Module 16, children continue to extend their understanding of two-dimensional shapes. Children show how larger shapes are composed from smaller shapes. This work leads into identifying whether the smaller shapes are equal size and shape. Children are then introduced to the concept of equal shares, partition circles and rectangles into two or four equal shares, and describe these equal shares as halves, quarters, or fourths. This is the conceptual basis for understanding fractions.

After Grade 1, children will extend their knowledge of partitioning rectangles and circles into halves, thirds, and fourths.

Mathematical Progressions Across the Grades

Prior Learning	Current Development	Future Connections
Children: • analyzed and compared two-dimensional shapes. • identified two-dimensional shapes. • composed simple shapes to form larger shapes.	**Children:** • show same-size shapes that make two-dimensional shapes. • partition circles and rectangles into two or four equal or unequal shares. • describe shares using the words *halves, half of, fourths, fourth of, quarters,* and *quarter, of.*	**Children:** • will recognize and draw shapes with specific attributes. • will partition circles and rectangles into two, three, or four equal shares. • will describe shares using the words *halves, thirds, half of, a third of,* etc.

TEACHER TO TEACHER
From the Classroom

Implement tasks that promote reasoning and problem solving. In first grade, I pose simple problems that require children to consider how to partition shapes into equal shares or parts. For example: Molly has two crackers, and she wants to share them equally with her three friends. How many crackers will Molly and each of her friends get? Some children might use concrete models and act it out. Other children will use drawings to solve this problem. Once I see most children have a solution, I bring the group together and we discuss their solutions. I ask meaningful questions to promote reasoning. I also help children begin to make sense of the vocabulary we use to discuss fractions, drawing attention to examples of when they use the terms correctly and labeling these examples so other children can learn. Children benefit from engaging in problem solving tasks that promote reasoning because it allows them to feel confident in their ability to solve problems on their own.

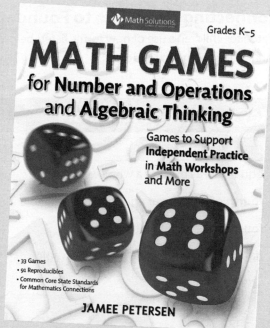

By giving all children regular exposure to language routines in context, you will provide opportunities for children to **listen for,** and **speak, read,** and **write** about mathematical situations. You will also give children the opportunity to develop understanding of both mathematical language and concepts.

Using Language Routines to Develop Understanding

Use the Professional Learning Cards for the following routines to plan for effective instruction.

Three Reads

Children read a problem or the teacher reads the problem three times with a specific focus each time.

1st Read What is the problem about?
2nd Read What do each of the numbers describe?
3rd Read What math questions could you ask about the problem?

Stronger and Clearer Each Time   Lesson 16.1

Children write or draw their reasoning about a problem, share that reasoning, explain it, listen to feedback, respond to feedback, and then refine their reasoning by writing or drawing again.

Compare and Connect   Lessons 16.1–16.4

Children listen to a partner's solution strategy, identify it, and then compare it to and contrast it with their own.

Critique, Correct, and Clarify

Children correct the work in a flawed explanation, argument, or solution method; share with a partner; and refine the sample work.

Connecting Language to Foundations for Fractions

Watch for children's use of new terms listed below as they explain their reasoning and make connections with new concepts.

Linguistic Note

Illustrate Understanding is an effective strategy for this module focusing on partitioning shapes into halves and fourths. Encourage children to talk about their drawings to build the necessary language skills to describe the parts of the shape.

Key Academic Vocabulary

Current Development • New Vocabulary

equal shares parts of a whole that are the same size

fourth of one of four equal parts of a whole

fourths four equal parts or shares

half of one of two equal parts of a whole

halves two equal parts or shares

quarter of one of four equal parts or shares

quarters four equal parts or shares

unequal shares parts of a whole that are not the same size

Module 16 Fraction Foundations

Seeking in the Garden!

How many shapes can you find that are the same size and shape?

Color the shapes that match the same color.

Check children's coloring.

Turn and Talk

If you put the matching shapes together, what shape does it make? See possible answer at the right.

Module 16   four hundred fifty-seven **457**

© Houghton Mifflin Harcourt Publishing Company

Seeking in the Garden!

Assess Prerequisite Concepts
Grade 1 Module 15

Have children complete the Module Opener Task. This task can be used to determine understanding of identifying shapes.

Engage Children

Have children work in mixed-ability groups to complete the task. This task is designed to:

- activate prior knowledge that is essential for success in the upcoming module.
- challenge children to think critically and justify their reasoning.
- encourage cooperation, collaboration, and discourse within a group.

Guide Children's Discussion

Listen for children who correctly use review vocabulary as part of their discourse. Children should be familiar with the terms *circle, square, triangle,* and *rectangle.* Ask children to explain what they mean if they use those terms.

Sample Guided Discussion:

Q **How do you identify that shapes are the same?**

Q **What new shapes can you make by putting other shapes together?**

Turn and Talk Discuss with children which matching two-dimensional shapes can be combined to make a larger shape. Possible answer: The two squares can be combined to make a rectangle.

Extend the Task

- Have children describe the shapes that make up other shapes, and the composite shape they make.

COMMON ERRORS

Verify that children identify same-sized shapes and understand they can be put together to make a new larger shape.

Watch for children who mark same shapes but different sizes. Have these children identify the rectangles on the page. **Ask:**

- How can you match the rectangles that are the same size?

Watch for children who do not identify shapes correctly. Have these children draw two-dimensional shapes they know. **Ask:**

- How did you know the name of the shape you drew?

Assign the Digital Are You Ready? to power actionable reports including
- proficiency by standards
- item analysis

Are You Ready?

Diagnostic Assessment

- Diagnose prerequisite mastery.
- Identify intervention needs.
- Modify or set up leveled groups.

Have children complete the *Are You Ready?* assessment on their own. Items test the prerequisites required to succeed with the new learning in this module.

Bigger and Smaller This item will assess whether children can identify shapes that are smaller.

Sort by Size This item will assess whether children can categorize shapes based on the attribute of size.

Draw Equal Groups This item will assess whether children can represent equal groups.

Name _____

Are You Ready?

Complete these problems to review prior concepts and skills you will need for this module.

Bigger and Smaller
Circle the shape that is smaller.

1   **2**

Sort by Size
Circle the shapes that are the same size.

3

Draw Equal Groups
Draw red stars to show an equal number of red stars and yellow stars.

4

Children should draw 6 red stars.

458 four hundred fifty-eight

DATA-DRIVEN INTERVENTION

 MTSS RtI

Concept/Skill	Objective	Prior Learning *	Intervene with
Bigger and Smaller	Compare shapes to identify which is smaller.	Grade K, Lesson 4.3	• Tier 3 Skill 13 • Reteach, Grade K, Lesson 4.3
Sort by Size	Sort same-size shapes into a group.	Grade K, Lesson 4.3	• Tier 2 Skill 20 • Reteach, Grade K, Lesson 4.3
Draw Equal Groups	Draw to show a group with the same number of stars as another group.	Grade K, Lesson 10.3	• Tier 2 Skill 6 • Reteach, Grade K, Lesson 10.3

* Your digital materials include access to resources? from Grades K–3. The lessons referenced here contain a variety of resources you can use with children who need support with this content.

16.1 Take Apart Two-Dimensional Shapes

LESSON FOCUS AND COHERENCE

■ Major □ Supporting ● Additional

Mathematics Standards

○ Partition circles and rectangles into two and four equal shares, describe the shares using the words *halves, fourths,* and *quarters,* and use the phrases *half of, fourth of,* and *quarter of.* Describe the whole as two of, or four of the shares. Understand for these examples that decomposing into more equal shares creates smaller shares.

Mathematical Practices and Processes

• Attend to precision.
• Look for and make use of structure.

I Can Objective

I can identify and represent how shapes that are the same size and shape can make circles and rectangles.

Learning Objective

Show same-size shapes within a circle or rectangle.

Language Objectives

• Explain how to recognize same-size shapes.
• Explain how to show same-size shapes within a shape.

Vocabulary

Review: circle, square

Lesson Materials: MathBoard, crayons, pencils, plane shapes, pattern blocks

Mathematical Progressions

Prior Learning	Current Development	Future Connections
Children: • identified circles, squares, and rectangles. **(GrK, 16.1, 16.2, 16.4)** • composed simple shapes. **(GrK, 16.6)**	**Children:** • represent same-size shapes that combine to make circles and rectangles.	**Children:** • will partition circles and rectangles. **(Gr2, 22.1–22.5)**

UNPACKING MATH STANDARDS

Partition circles and rectangles into two and four equal shares, describe the shares using the words *halves, fourths,* and *quarters,* and use the phrases *half of, fourth of,* and *quarter of.* Describe the whole as two of, or four of the shares. Understand for these examples that decomposing into more equal shares creates smaller shares.

What It Means to You

In this foundational lesson, children demonstrate how to decompose a circle or rectangle to show parts of equal size. The approach in this lesson, and the remaining lessons in this module, helps children begin to develop a conceptual basis for understanding fractions.

ACTIVATE PRIOR KNOWLEDGE • Combine Shapes

Use these activities to quickly assess and activate prior knowledge as needed.

Math Routine

Number of the Day Today's number is 8. How many different ways can you find to combine 8 squares? Can you find a way to combine 8 squares so your new shape has 8 sides?

Have children use their MathBoard to draw squares or use square pattern blocks or plane shapes to make combined shapes. Invite children who have made different 8-square combined shapes to share with the class. Have children count the sides of the combined shapes they made. Do any of their combined shapes have 8 sides? Have the class offer suggestions for rearranging the shapes to make an 8-sided shape. (It can be done.)

Make Connections

Based on children's responses to the Math Routine, choose one of the following:

1 Project the Interactive Reteach, Grade 1, Lesson 15.3.

2 Complete the Prerequisite Skills Activity:

Have pairs of children use pattern blocks or plane shapes to compose a shape. Discuss with children what smaller shapes are put together to make the larger shape.

SHARPEN SKILLS

If time permits, use this on-level activity to build fluency and practice basic skills.

Vocabulary Review

Children work in small groups. Taking turns, one child draws a shape on their MathBoard without showing it to the group. They describe their shape aloud, and the others in the group use the description to identify and draw that shape. Children compare their drawings and discuss what other descriptions might have been used to make their drawings more alike.

PLAN FOR DIFFERENTIATED INSTRUCTION

 MTSS RtI

Small-Group Options

Use these teacher-guided activities with pulled small groups at the teacher table.

On Track

Materials: MathBoard, plane shapes

Have one child decide whether to combine two or four of the same shape to make a larger shape. The other members of the group make a shape with the designated number of shapes. When everyone is finished, have the group members discuss their combined shapes.

• How are your combined shapes alike?

• How are your combined shapes different?

Almost There (RtI)

Materials: MathBoard, plane shapes, Two-Dimensional Shapes (Teacher Resource Masters), pattern blocks

Use this Tabletop Flipchart Mini-Lesson to guide children in partitioning shapes. Have children work together to find ways that a square can be made by combining two same-size shapes. Have them draw examples on their MathBoards. Then have children find ways that a square can be made by combining four same-size shapes.

Tabletop Flipchart:
Lesson 16.1

Mini-Lesson

Ready for More

Materials: MathBoard

Have children draw to show how to compose different-sized circles, squares, and rectangles in different ways. Children can compare their drawings with others in the group. Discuss the attributes of each shape that is a part of the larger shape.

Math Center Options

Use these student self-directed activities at centers or stations. **Key:** ● **Print Resources** ● **Online Resources**

On Track

●● More Practice/Homework 16.1
● Interactive Glossary: **circle**, **square**
● Game: Build It

Almost There

● Reteach 16.1
● Interactive Reteach 16.1

Ready for More

● Challenge 16.1
● Interactive Challenge 16.1

Unit Project Check children's progress by asking how being able to identify how shapes are combined to make larger shapes can help them design their own flags.

ONLINE Ed   View data-driven grouping recommendations and assign differentiation resources.

During the *Spark Your Learning,* listen and watch for strategies students use. See samples of student work on this page.

Draw Straight Lines to Show Shapes — Strategy 1

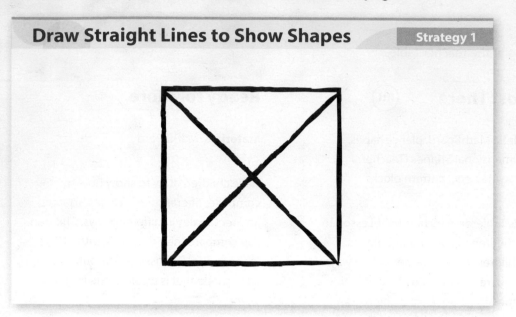

If children . . . draw lines to show shapes in the square, they are demonstrating exemplary understanding of showing composite shapes and making connections to what they learned in Module 15.

Have these children . . . share what shapes they made in the square. **Ask:**

Q How do you describe the shapes in the square?

Q What new shapes did you make?

Draw One Straight Line — Strategy 2

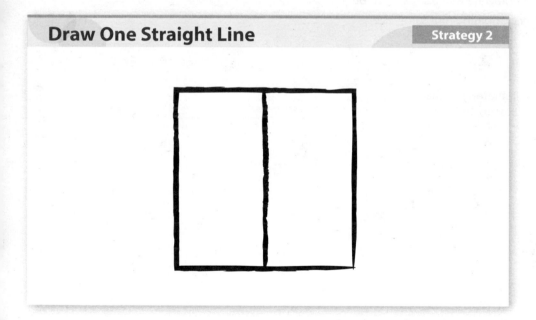

If children . . . draw one line inside the square, they demonstrate showing smaller shapes that make up a larger shape.

Activate prior knowledge . . . by encouraging them to draw additional straight lines to show more than one shape inside the square. **Ask:**

Q How can you draw another straight line to also show triangles inside your square?

COMMON ERROR: Does Not Show Shapes in the Square

If children . . . do not draw lines that connect with the given square, they may not understand that the new shapes must be closed figures.

Then intervene . . . by reminding them to start and end the lines on the inside border of the square. **Ask:**

Q How can you draw a straight line to connect the corners of the square?

Q How could you draw a straight line to connect sides of the square?

Name _____

Take Apart Two-Dimensional Shapes

(I Can) identify and represent how shapes that are the same size and shape can make circles and rectangles.

Spark Your Learning

Draw straight lines to make shapes inside the square.

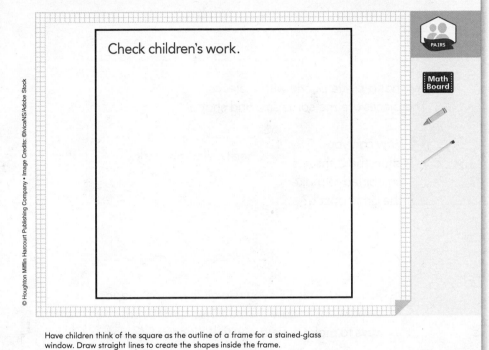

Check children's work.

PAIRS

Math Board

Have children think of the square as the outline of a frame for a stained-glass window. Draw straight lines to create the shapes inside the frame.

---

① Spark Your Learning

▶ MOTIVATE

The image on the page is of a stained-glass window. Ask children if they have seen stained-glass windows anywhere else. Discuss the differences between the stained-glass image on the page and ones children may have seen in real life.

EL CONNECT MATH IDEAS, REASONING, AND LANGUAGE Compare and Connect

Remind children they are familiar with two-dimensional shapes having straight sides such as squares and rectangles. Before starting the task, you can have children list some two-dimensional shapes made from straight sides. Have partners share their work and then compare and contrast the shape attributes.

▶ PERSEVERE

If children need additional support, guide them by asking:

Q Assessing Where will your lines start and stop? Possible answer: They will start and stop on the sides or vertices on the square.

Q Advancing • Use Tools What tool could you use to solve the problem? Why is the tool you chose the one that works for you? Childrens' choices of strategies or tools will vary.

Q Advancing How do you know the new shapes you made will fit together to make a square? Possible answer: All fit inside the square without overlap or gaps.

Q Advancing What shapes did you make? Children may not know the names of all of the shapes. Suggest having children color the shapes they do know.

Turn and Talk How did you know what lines to draw to show new shapes? Discuss with children that it helps to have a plan before they begin to draw the lines. Possible answer: I knew I could make 2 triangles by drawing a line between opposite corners of the square.

▶ BUILD SHARED UNDERSTANDING

Select children who used various strategies and tools to share with the class how they solved the problem. Have children discuss why they chose a specific strategy or tool.

② Learn Together

Build Understanding

Tasks 1 and 2 **(MP)** **Use Structure** Read the first problem aloud. Discuss that the image shown is a sample to show a puzzle made from 4 pieces the same size and shape, but it is not a square. Make sure children understand they will be showing how to combine 4 shapes to make a square. After completing the first task, children then continue on to combine 2 same-size shapes to make a circle. You may want to provide pattern blocks or plane shapes for children to use.

Sample Guided Discussion:

Q **How will you show the puzzle?** Possible answer: I can draw the outline of the puzzle and then draw straight lines to show the shapes. I need to show shapes inside the puzzle that are all the same size and shape.

Q **How do you know that shapes of the pieces of the puzzle are the same size and shape?** Possible answers: I traced around a square pattern block; I drew a circle and then drew one line down the center so both sides are the same.

Turn and Talk Encourage children to share their work. Discuss how there are many ways to combine shapes to make new shapes. Possible answer: Yes. I put 4 squares together to make a bigger square.

Build Understanding

Sam has a **square** puzzle with 4 pieces. The pieces are the same size and shape.

A How can you show the 4 shapes combined to make the square puzzle?

Check children's work.

Ava has a **circle** puzzle with 2 pieces. The pieces are the same size and shape.

B How can you show the 2 shapes combined to make the circle puzzle?

Check children's work.

Turn and Talk Did you use all the same shapes to make the square puzzle? Discuss different ways to make a square with 4 pieces. See possible answer at the left.

LEVELED QUESTIONS

Depth of Knowledge (DOK)	Leveled Questions	What Does This Tell You?
Level 1 **Recall**	How can you use two squares to make a rectangle? Possible answer: I can put 2 squares side by side to make a rectangle.	Children's answers will show that they know what shapes compose another.
Level 2 **Basic Application of Skills & Concepts**	What different shapes can you use to make a square? Possible answer: I can combine 4 triangles to make a square.	Children's answers will show that they know how to compose a two-dimensional shape with other two-dimensional shapes.
Level 3 **Strategic Thinking & Complex Reasoning**	Why is there more than one way to combine shapes to make another shape? Possible answer: There is more than one way that shapes can fit together.	Children's answers will demonstrate that they understand that two-dimensional shapes can be used to make different shapes.

Name _____

How can you draw lines to show shapes combined to make a circle? Each shape is the same size.

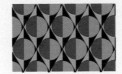

A Draw a line to show 2 shapes that are the same size.
Possible answer:

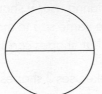

B Draw 2 lines to show 4 shapes that are the same size. Possible answer:

Check Understanding

Draw triangles, squares, or rectangles to make the shape.

1 Sergio uses 2 shapes that are the same size and shape to make a rectangle.

Show 2 shapes he could use to make the rectangle.

What shapes did you use? Possible answer: 2 rectangles

Possible answer:

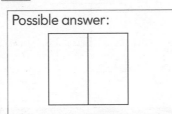

© Houghton Mifflin Harcourt Publishing Company • Image Credits: ©ellinadesign/Shutterstock

---

Task 3 (MP) **Attend to Precision** Read the problem aloud. Remind children that when they draw their lines, the shapes inside the circle should be the same size. You may want to suggest that children practice on their MathBoard first, before making their final drawings.

Sample Guided Discussion:

Q **How can you draw a line in the circle to make two shapes the same size?** I can draw a line from one point on the circle to another point on the circle that goes through the center of the circle.

Q **How do you make four shapes the same size?** Possible answer: I can draw 2 lines that show 4 shapes that when put together are the same size.

(EL) **OPTIMIZE OUTPUT**
Stronger and Clearer

Have children share their drawings with a partner. Remind children to ask questions of each other that focus on explaining how they drew lines to show shapes that are the same size and shape. Then, have them refine their answers.

data checkpoint

---

③ Check Understanding

Formative Assessment

Use formative assessment to determine if your students are successful with this lesson's learning objective.

Children who successfully complete the Check Understanding can continue to the On Your Own practice.

For children who missed the Check Understanding problem, work in a pulled small group with the Tabletop Flipchart Mini-Lesson.

ONLINE [Ed] **Assign the Digital Check Understanding to determine**
• success with the learning objective
• items to review
• grouping and differentiation resources

④ Differentiation Options

Differentiate instruction for all children using small group mini-lessons and math center activities on page 459C.

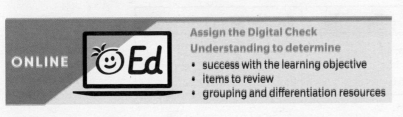

Reteach

Challenge

Assign the Digital On Your Own for
• built-in student supports
• Actionable Item Reports
• Standards Analysis Reports

On Your Own

■ **Problems 2–3 • Use Structure** Children demonstrate how to show shapes inside a circle and rectangle that are the same size and shape by drawing lines.

■ **Problems 4–5** Children demonstrate how to draw same-size shapes that compose a given shape.

⑤ Wrap-Up

Summarize learning with your class. Consider using the Exit Ticket, Put It in Writing, or I Can scale.

Exit Ticket

Draw a square that has been made by two shapes that are the same size and shape.

Check children's drawings.

Put It in Writing

Explain how you can draw lines in a square to make four shapes that are the same size.

I Can

The scale below can help you and your students understand their progress on a learning goal.

4	I can show and explain how circles and rectangles can be made from two or four same-size shapes.
3	I can identify and represent how shapes that are the same size and shape can make circles and rectangles.
2	I can draw lines to show how a two-dimensional shape is put together from other shapes.
1	I can make a concrete model to show how to put same-size shapes together.

On Your Own

(MP) **Use Structure** Draw lines to show the shapes.

Possible answers:

2 Brianna uses 4 shapes that are the same size to make a circle. What shapes can she use?

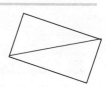

3 Jake uses 2 shapes that are the same size to make a rectangle. What shapes can he use?

Draw triangles, squares, or rectangles to make the shape.

4 Draw 4 shapes the same size and shape to make a square.
Possible answer:

5 Draw 2 shapes the same size and shape to make a rectangle.
Possible answer:

© Houghton Mifflin Harcourt Publishing Company

🎲 I'm in a **Learning Mindset!**

What made the directions clear to me?

Keep Going 🔟▶ Practice and Homework Journal

Learning Mindset

Try Again Learns Effectively

Help children determine the type of support they need for understanding the directions for the problems in this lesson. *Do you understand what to do simply by reading the directions? Or is it more helpful if someone else reads them or walks through an example? When the directions are clear to you, it is more likely that you will be able to complete your work successfully. Be sure to ask for help understanding the directions if you do not know what to do.*

Assignment Guide

Reference the chart below for problems associated with tasks. In a 2-day lesson, reference the chart to assign daily homework.

Learn Together Tasks	On Your Own Problems
Tasks 1–2, p. 460	Problems 4 and 5
Task 3, p. 461	Problems 2 and 3

Take Apart Two-Dimensional Shapes

LESSON 16.1
**More Practice/
Homework**

 **ONLINE**
Video Tutorials and
Interactive Examples

(MP) Use Structure Draw lines to show the shapes.
Possible answers shown.

1 Charlie uses 4 shapes that are the same size to make a rectangle.

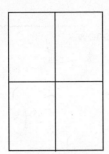

2 Frank uses 2 shapes that are the same size to make a square.

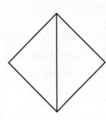

(MP) Attend to Precision Draw triangles, squares, or rectangles to make the shape.
Check children's work. Possible drawings shown.

3 Draw 2 shapes the same size and shape to make a rectangle.

4 Draw 4 shapes the same size and shape to make a square.

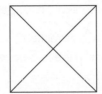

Module 16 • Lesson 1   one hundred seventy-five **P175**

ONLINE

 **Assign the Digital More Practice/
Homework for**

• built-in student supports
• Actionable Item Reports
• Standards Analysis Reports

More Practice/Homework

Take Apart Two-Dimensional Shapes

Use More Practice/Homework pages to provide children with additional practice applying the concepts and skills presented in the lesson.

■ **Problems 1–2 • Use Structure** Children draw lines to show shapes that are the same size to make the rectangle and square.

■ **Problems 3–4 • Attend to Precision** Children draw same-size shapes that compose a given shape.

Assignment Guide

Reference the chart below for problems associated with tasks. In a 2-day lesson, reference the chart to assign daily homework.

Learn Together Tasks	More Practice/Homework Problems
Tasks 1–2, p. 460	Problems 3 and 4
Task 3, p. 461	Problems 1–2 and 5–6

Test Prep

The Test Prep items provided assess understanding of composing two-dimensional shapes that are the same size.

Additional Test Prep opportunities are available online and in *Getting Ready for High Stakes Assessment*.

Spiral Review

The spiral review problems will help determine if children have retained information taught in the past. Here, children will need to demonstrate an ability to draw and describe two-dimensional shapes. **(15.2)**

Test Prep

Fill in the bubble next to the correct answer.

5 Nala draws lines in a rectangle to show 4 shapes that are the same size. Which is her shape?

 ○   ○   ●

6 Simon draws a line in a circle to show 2 shapes that are the same size. Which is his shape?

○ ● ○

Spiral Review   Accept reasonable drawings.

7 Draw to show a hexagon.

How many sides does a hexagon have? ___6___

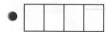

8 Draw to show a trapezoid.

How many vertices does a trapezoid have? ___4___

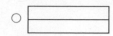

ANCHOR-CHART OPTION

As you progress through the module, build and display an anchor chart.

(EL) **Connect Math Ideas, Reasoning, and Language Collect and Display**

Have children build their own anchor chart in their Practice and Homework Journal. A completed chart for the module is shown here.

Show Shares of Shapes

4 unequal shares

2 equal shares — halves

1 large square made of 4 small squares

4 equal shares

1 fourth or 1 quarter

16.2 Identify Equal or Unequal Shares

LESSON FOCUS AND COHERENCE

■ Major   ☐ Supporting   ● Additional

Mathematics Standards

○ Partition circles and rectangles into two and four equal shares, describe the shares using the words *halves, fourths,* and *quarters,* and use the phrases *half of, fourth of,* and *quarter of.* Describe the whole as two of, or four of the shares. Understand for these examples that decomposing into more equal shares creates smaller shares.

Mathematical Practices and Processes

- Construct viable arguments and critique the reasoning of others.
- Attend to precision.
- Look for and make use of structure.

I Can Objective

I can identify and represent equal shares and unequal shares in circles and rectangles.

Learning Objective

Identify equal or unequal shares in a circle or rectangle.

Language Objectives

- Explain how to determine equal shares and unequal shares.
- Explain how to show equal and unequal shares.

Vocabulary

New: equal shares, unequal shares

Lesson Materials: Equal and Unequal Shares Cards (Teacher Resource Masters), MathBoard, pencils, crayons, scissors

Mathematical Progressions

Prior Learning	Current Development	Future Connections
Children: • identified circles, squares, and rectangles. **(GrK, 16.1, 16.2, 16.4)** • composed simple shapes. **(GrK, 16.6)** • compared shapes. **(GrK, 16.7)**	**Children:** • identify equal shares and unequal shares in circles and rectangles. • represent two or four equal or unequal shares in circles and rectangles.	**Children:** • will identify, describe, and draw two, three, or four equal shares. **(Gr2, 22.2–22.3)** • will use different ways to show two, three, or four equal shares. **(Gr2, 22.5)**

UNPACKING MATH STANDARDS

Partition circles and rectangles into two and four equal shares, describe the shares using the words *halves, fourths,* and *quarters,* and use the phrases *half of, fourth of,* and *quarter of.* Describe the whole as two of, or four of the shares. Understand for these examples that decomposing into more equal shares creates smaller shares.

What It Means to You

Children will show two and four parts in circles and rectangles. They will be able to identify whether the parts or shares are equal or unequal, which is foundational to the understanding of fractions because fractions are based on a whole being divided into equal parts. Limiting the number of parts to two or four gives children the opportunity to work with parts or shares that are halves and fourths (or quarters) before naming them as such. Throughout the lesson, children determine whether the shares are equal, which will lead them to determine in the next lessons whether they can describe the shares as halves or fourths (quarters).

WARM-UP OPTIONS

ACTIVATE PRIOR KNOWLEDGE • Partition Shapes

Use these activities to quickly assess and activate prior knowledge as needed.

Math Routine

Which One Doesn't Belong? Which shape does not belong? Explain your reasoning.

Reveal the group of squares. Ask a child to share which image they feel does not belong and explain their reasoning. Ask if anyone else in the class chose the same image and why they felt it did not belong. Repeat with a child who has selected a different image. Encourage the other children to ask questions and critique each explanation. There is no one correct answer, so look for well-reasoned explanations from children.

Make Connections

Based on children's response to the Math Routine, choose one of the following:

1 Project the Interactive Reteach, Grade 1, Lesson 16.1.

2 Complete the Prerequisite Skills Activity:

Have children use pattern blocks or plane shapes to compose rectangles and circles. Encourage children to use shapes that are the same size to compose the shapes. You may want to have children trace around the shapes to show how each smaller shape that composes the larger shape is the same size.

SHARPEN SKILLS

If time permits, use this on-level activity to build fluency and practice basic skills.

Fluency—Add Within 10

Objective: Children make picture cards to practice math facts within 10.

Materials: Fluency Builder: Addition Level 4 (Differentiated Instruction Blackline Masters), index cards, markers

Have children work in pairs to make picture cards using index cards and markers. On each card, they should draw a number of objects from one to five. When they are finished, have them mix up the cards and place them facedown between them. Children should take turns choosing a card. They can work together to find how many more they need to add to make 10.

Children can then complete the Fluency Builder worksheet to practice addition within 10.

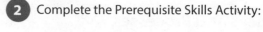

Name _____ Fluency Builder
Addition Level 4

Find the unknown number.

1	$3 + 2 = \underline{5}$	2	$2 + 5 = \underline{7}$
3	$2 + \underline{1} = 3$	4	$3 + \underline{3} = 6$
5	$\underline{5} + 3 = 8$	6	$\underline{2} + 6 = 8$
7	$6 + \underline{3} = 9$	8	$\underline{8} + 2 = 10$

| 9 | $\begin{array}{r}4\\+3\\\hline7\end{array}$ | 10 | $\begin{array}{r}2\\+7\\\hline9\end{array}$ | 11 | $\begin{array}{r}6\\+4\\\hline10\end{array}$ | 12 | $\begin{array}{r}5\\+4\\\hline9\end{array}$ |
| 13 | $\begin{array}{r}1\\+3\\\hline4\end{array}$ | 14 | $\begin{array}{r}5\\+0\\\hline5\end{array}$ | 15 | $\begin{array}{r}7\\+1\\\hline8\end{array}$ | 16 | $\begin{array}{r}3\\+7\\\hline10\end{array}$ |

224 two hundred twenty-four   BUILDING FLUENCY

PLAN FOR DIFFERENTIATED INSTRUCTION

MTSS RtI

Small-Group Options

Use these teacher-guided activities with pulled small groups at the teacher table.

On Track

Materials: index cards, markers

Select some children to draw shapes that show two shares and some to draw shapes that show four shares. Have each child make two cards, one with a shape that has equal shares and one with a shape that has unequal shares. After mixing up the cards, have the group work together to sort the cards into two piles: equal shares and unequal shares. **Ask:**

- How do you know when the shares are equal? Possible answer: They are the same size.

- How can you be sure that shares are equal or unequal? Possible answer: You can compare the size of the shapes.

Almost There RtI

Materials: Equal and Unequal Shares Cards (Teacher Resource Masters), construction paper

Use this Tabletop Flipchart Mini-Lesson to guide children in showing equal and unequal shares. Have children cut out a rectangle. Challenge them to work together to find different ways to fold the shape to show equal shares. **Ask:**

- How do you know when the shares are equal?

- How did you know how to fold so that the shares are unequal?

Tabletop Flipchart:
Lesson 16.2

Mini-Lesson

Ready for More

Materials: MathBoard

Have children draw examples of equal and unequal shares on their MathBoards. Then each child must explain to the others in the group why the drawing shows equal or unequal shares. **Ask:**

- How can you be confident that the shares are equal? Possible answer: I can look at them and see if they are the same size.

- What evidence can you give that the shares are unequal? Possible answer: If they are not the same size, then they are not equal shares.

Math Center Options

Use these student self-directed activities at centers or stations.   **Key:** ● Print Resources ● Online Resources

On Track

- ●● More Practice/Homework 16.2
- ● Fluency Builder: Addition Level 4
- ● Interactive Glossary: **equal shares**, **unequal shares**
- ● My Learning Summary

Almost There

- ● Reteach 16.2
- ● Interactive Reteach 16.2

Ready for More

- ● Challenge 16.2
- ● Interactive Challenge 16.2

ONLINE ⬤Ed   View data-driven grouping recommendations and assign differentiation resources.

During the *Spark Your Learning,* listen and watch for strategies students use. See samples of student work on this page.

Sort Shapes as Equal or Unequal Parts   Strategy 1

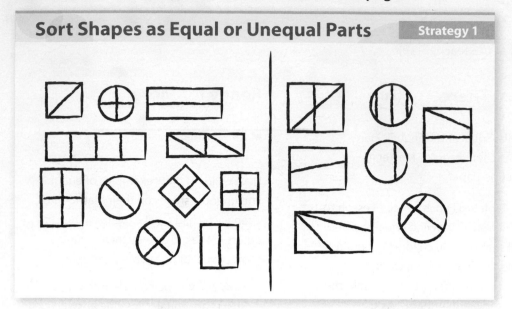

If children . . . sorted the cards into groups showing parts of equal size and parts of unequal size, they are demonstrating exemplary understanding of equal and unequal parts. Note: Children do not have to draw to show each card.

Have these children . . . share how they grouped the cards. **Ask:**

Q How could you tell if the parts put together to make the whole were the same size?

Sort Shapes by Number of Parts   Strategy 2

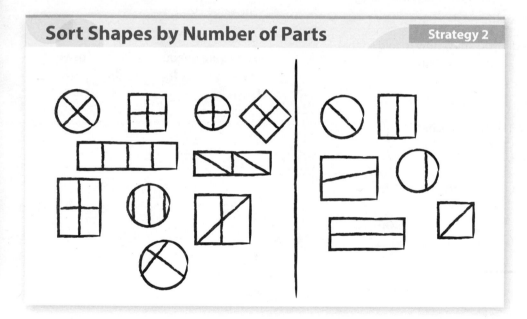

If children . . . sort the cards according to the number of parts, they may need encouragement to analyze the cards to notice shapes composed of identical smaller shapes. Note: Children do not have to draw to show each card.

Activate prior knowledge . . . by encouraging them to look at the size and shape of the parts in each figure. **Ask:**

Q Is there another way that you could have sorted the cards?

Q What do you notice that is the same about some of the parts of the whole shapes?

COMMON ERROR: Indeterminate Sort

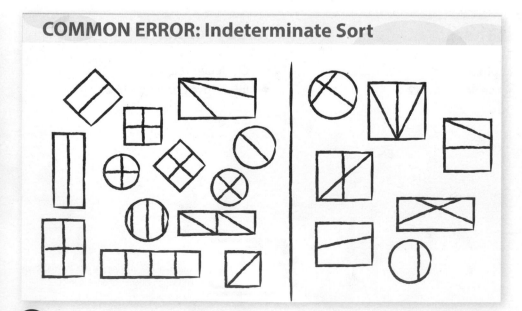

If children . . . do not sort with any apparent strategy, then they may not understand how to sort. Note: Children do not have to draw to show each card.

Then intervene . . . by encouraging them to look for ways the shapes are similar. **Ask:**

Q When you look at the smaller parts in a larger shape, how are the parts alike? How are the parts different?

Q How can you group them into two groups to show something that is the same about the shapes?

Name _____

Identify Equal or Unequal Shares

(I Can) identify and represent equal shares and unequal shares in circles and rectangles.

Spark Your Learning

How can you sort the shapes into groups?

Check children's work.

Children could have grouped the shapes by: number of shares, equal shares/not equal shares, shapes.

Provide the Equal and Unequal Shares Cards for pairs to use. Have children sort the cards into groups. Then have the children write or draw to show how they grouped the shapes.

Module 16 • Lesson 2
four hundred sixty-three 463

---

① Spark Your Learning

▶ MOTIVATE

Before beginning the lesson, have pairs of children cut out one set of the Equal and Unequal Shares Cards from the Teacher Resource Masters. Ask the pairs of children to decide how to place the shapes into groups.

(EL) CONNECT MATH IDEAS, REASONING, AND LANGUAGE Compare and Connect
Remind children they are familiar with sorting shapes by sides and vertices. Before starting the task, discuss some of the shapes on the cards. Have partners share how they grouped the shapes and then compare and contrast.

▶ PERSEVERE

If children need support, guide them by asking:

Q Assessing How are you sorting the shapes on the cards? Answers will vary. Possible answer: circles and rectangles

Q Advancing Is there another way to group the cards? Possible answer: Yes, instead of grouping by shape, we could group them by number of parts.

Q Advancing What do you notice about the parts of some of the shapes? Possible answer: Some shapes show sections that are all the same size and shape.

Q Advancing • Use Tools Choose a shape that has two parts that are the same size. **Ask:** How can you show four parts that are the same size on that shape? Possible answer: I can draw a new line inside the shape to show 4 parts that are the same size.

▶ BUILD SHARED UNDERSTANDING

Select children who used various strategies and tools to share with the class how they solved the problem. Have children discuss why they chose a specific strategy or tool.

② Learn Together

Build Understanding

Task 1 **MP** **Use Structure** Read the problem aloud. Ask children how the features of a square might help them decide how to solve both parts of the task.

CONNECT TO VOCABULARY

Have children use their **Interactive Glossary** during this conversation to record their understanding.

 CONNECT MATH IDEAS, REASONING, AND LANGUAGE Compare and Connect

Have children use their own words to describe **equal shares** and **unequal shares**. Have partners discuss how their descriptions compare and contrast.

Sample Guided Discussion:

Q **Why can the two pictures you drew both show equal shares (or equal parts) of a square? Explain.** Possible answer: Even though the two pictures show different shapes, the 4 shares (or parts) inside each square are all the same size and shape.

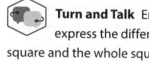 **Turn and Talk** Encourage children to clearly express the difference between the parts of the square and the whole square. Possible answer: The parts are smaller than the whole because the 4 parts are combined to make 1 whole.

Build Understanding

A Jake plants a square garden. He separates the garden into 4 equal shares.

Show how the garden could look.

Check children's work.
Possible answer:

> Math Board

B Show equal shares of a square garden in a different way.

Check children's work.
Possible answer:

 Turn and Talk Are the shares smaller or larger than the whole square garden? Explain. See possible answer at the left.

Connect to Vocabulary

equal shares:

unequal shares:

LEVELED QUESTIONS

Depth of Knowledge (DOK)	Leveled Questions	What Does This Tell You?
Level 1 **Recall**	What is an equal share or equal part? Possible answer: when the shares, or parts, are the same size	Children's answers will show that they understand the definition of equal shares.
Level 2 **Basic Application of Skills & Concepts**	How can you show four equal shares in a square? Possible answer: I can first make 2 equal shares, and then make 2 equal shares in each of those shares.	Children's answers will demonstrate that they can draw equal shares.
Level 3 **Strategic Thinking & Complex Reasoning**	Can a square show both equal shares and unequal shares? Possible answer: No, because if only some of the parts are the same size, then the whole shape shows unequal shares.	Children's answers will show that they have an understanding of how shapes can show shares.

Step It Out

1 Draw a rectangle with 4 equal shares.
Possible answer:

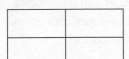

2 Draw a rectangle with 4 unequal shares.
Possible answer:

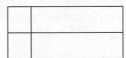

··

Check Understanding **Math Board** Possible lines shown.

Draw lines to show equal shares or unequal shares.

1 Andrea cut a square sandwich into 4 equal shares. Show how Andrea could cut the square.

2 2 unequal shares

3 2 equal shares

4 Which shape shows unequal shares? Circle the shape.

Step It Out

Tasks 2 and 3 **MP** **Attend to Precision** Read the problems to children and discuss the differences between equal shares and unequal shares. Remind children to draw so their pictures clearly show equal shares or unequal shares.

Sample Guided Discussion:

Q **How can you draw four equal shares?** Possible answer: I can draw lines from the center of each side to the center of another side.

Q **What will you do differently to draw four unequal shares?** Possible answer: I will draw lines to show 4 parts, but the parts will not all be the same size.

data
checkpoint

③ Check Understanding

Formative Assessment

Use formative assessment to determine if your students are successful with this lesson's learning objective.

Children who successfully complete the Check Understanding can continue to the On Your Own practice.

For children who miss 1 problem or more, work in a pulled small group with the Tabletop Flipchart Mini-Lesson.

ONLINE **Ed** Assign the Digital Check Understanding to determine
• success with the learning objective
• items to review
• grouping and differentiation resources

④ Differentiation Options

Differentiate instruction for all children using small group mini-lessons and math center activities on page 463C.

Reteach

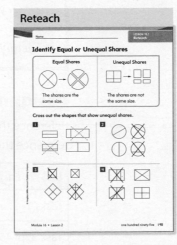

Challenge

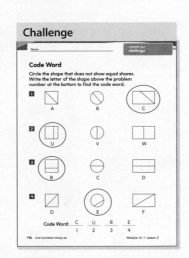

Assign the Digital On Your Own for
• built-in student supports
• Actionable Item Reports
• Standards Analysis Reports

On Your Own

■ **Problems 5–6 • Construct Arguments** Children demonstrate understanding of how to draw lines to show equal or unequal shares. Then they write to justify their reasoning.

■ **Problem 7 • Open Ended** Children demonstrate that there are multiple ways to show equal shares.

 **Wrap-Up**

Summarize learning with your class. Consider using the Exit Ticket, Put It in Writing, or I Can scale.

Exit Ticket

Draw a circle. Then draw a line in the circle to show two unequal shares. Check children's drawings.

Put It in Writing

Explain the difference between equal and unequal shares.

I Can

The scale below can help you and your students understand their progress on a learning goal.

4	I can explain why shares are equal or unequal and draw to represent equal and unequal shares in shapes.
3	I can identify and represent equal shares and unequal shares in circles and rectangles.
2	I can identify equal and unequal shares in circles and rectangles.
1	I can identify same-size shapes.

On Your Own

Draw a line to show equal or unequal shares. Possible answers shown.

5 Milo has a square. How can he use a line to make 2 equal shares?

(MP) Construct Arguments
How do you know that the shares are equal?

Possible answer: The shares are the same size.

6 How can Milo make 2 unequal shares on his square?

(MP) Construct Arguments
How do you know that the shares are unequal?

Possible answer: The shares are not the same size.

7 Open Ended In Problem 5, you made 2 equal shares. What is another way to show 2 equal shares? Possible answer:

🎲 I'm in a **Learning Mindset !**

What do I do when I do not know what to do?

_____

Learning Mindset

Try Again Getting Unstuck

Remind children that in the last module you discussed asking questions as a strategy for getting unstuck. Have children brainstorm additional strategies for getting unstuck. *Can you think of strategies other than asking questions for getting unstuck? Another way to get unstuck is to work with a partner. When you work with a partner you are always talking about your ideas and your reasoning. A partner may take a completely different approach to the problem than you do. What are other ways of getting unstuck?*

Assignment Guide

Reference the chart below for problems associated with tasks. In a 2-day lesson, reference the chart to assign daily homework.

Learn Together Tasks	On Your Own Problems
Tasks 1–2, pp. 464–465	Problems 5 and 7
Task 3, p. 465	Problem 6

LESSON 16.2
**More Practice/
Homework**

 **ONLINE**
Video Tutorials and
Interactive Examples

Identify Equal or Unequal Shares

Possible drawings shown.

1 Draw lines to show
4 equal shares.

(MP) Construct Arguments

How do you know the
shares are equal?

Possible answer: The shares
are all the same size.

2 Draw lines to show
4 unequal shares.

(MP) Construct Arguments

How do you know the
shares are unequal?

Possible answer: The shares
are not all the same size.

Write equal shares or unequal shares.

3

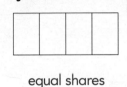

equal shares

4

unequal shares

Math on the Spot Write the number of equal shares.

5

__4__ equal shares

6

__2__ equal shares

ONLINE

Assign the Digital More Practice/
Homework for

• built-in student supports
• Actionable Item Reports
• Standards Analysis Reports

More Practice/Homework

Identify Equal or Unequal Shares

Use More Practice/Homework pages to provide children
with additional practice applying the concepts and skills
presented in the lesson.

■ **Problems 1–2 • Construct Arguments** Children
demonstrate understanding of equal and unequal shares
by first drawing and then explaining how the shape
shows equal shares or unequal shares.

■ **Problems 3–4** Children identify equal or unequal shares.

Math on the Spot

Encourage children to complete
Problems 5–6 and then review their
work with a family member or a
friend by watching the *Math on the
Spot* video.

Assignment Guide

Reference the chart below for problems associated with tasks. In a 2-day lesson,
reference the chart to assign daily homework.

Learn Together Tasks	More Practice/Homework Problems
Tasks 1–2, p. 464–465	Problems 1 and 8–9
Task 2–3, p. 465	Problems 3–6
Task 3, p. 465	Problems 2 and 7

Test Prep

The Test Prep items provided assess understanding of determining if shares are equal or unequal.

Additional Test Prep opportunities are available online and in *Getting Ready for High Stakes Assessment.*

Spiral Review

The spiral review problem will help determine if children have retained information taught in the past. Here, children will need to demonstrate an ability to sort two-dimensional shapes by attributes. **(15.1)**

Test Prep

Fill in the bubble next to the correct answer.

7 Which does this shape show?

- ○ 2 equal shares
- ● 2 unequal shares
- ○ 4 unequal shares

8 Which does this shape show?

- ○ 2 equal shares
- ● 4 equal shares
- ○ 4 unequal shares

9 Which shape shows 2 equal shares?

 ○   ○   ●

Spiral Review

10 Circle the shapes with only 3 vertices.
Draw a line under the shapes with 4 sides.

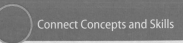

16.3 Partition Shapes into Halves

LESSON FOCUS AND COHERENCE

■ Major ☐ Supporting ● Additional

Mathematics Standards

○ Partition circles and rectangles into two and four equal shares, describe the shares using the words *halves, fourths,* and *quarters,* and use the phrases *half of, fourth of,* and *quarter of.* Describe the whole as two of, or four of the shares. Understand for these examples that decomposing into more equal shares creates smaller shares.

Mathematical Practices and Processes

- Construct viable arguments and critique the reasoning of others.
- Attend to precision.
- Look for and make use of structure.

I Can Objective

I can identify and represent halves of circles and rectangles.

Learning Objectives

Separate circles and rectangles into halves and describe the whole as two of the shares.

Language Objectives

- Explain how many halves are in a whole.
- Explain the meaning of *half of* and *halves.*

Vocabulary

New: half of, halves

Lesson Materials: MathBoard, crayons, pencils, Two-Dimensional Shapes (Teacher Resource Masters)

Mathematical Progressions

Prior Learning	Current Development	Future Connections
Children: • identified circles, squares, and rectangles. **(GrK, 16.1, 16.2, 16.4)** • composed simple shapes. **(GrK, 16.6)**	**Children:** • partition circles and rectangles into two equal shares. • identify two equal shares as halves. • understand that half of a shape is smaller than the whole shape.	**Children:** • will identify, describe, and draw two, three, or four equal shares. **(Gr2, 22.2–22.3)** • will identify these equal shares as halves, thirds, and fourths (quarters). **(Gr2, 22.2–22.3)** • will use different ways to show halves, thirds, and fourths (quarters). **(Gr2, 22.5)**

PROFESSIONAL LEARNING

About the Math

Why Teach This? Practice showing equal shares of rectangles and circles helps children develop a foundational understanding of halves. Emphasis is placed on the shares being equal shares. While limited at this time to two shares, the basic concept that shares must be equal applies to every number of shares connected with fractions. As children use visual models to represent halves, they are establishing a foundation and building their conception of fractions.

ACTIVATE PRIOR KNOWLEDGE • Equal Shares

Use these activities to quickly assess and activate prior knowledge as needed.

Math Routine

True or False? Does the shape show equal shares? If the shape shows equal shares, say *true*. If the shape shows unequal shares, say *false*. How could you change the shapes that show unequal shares to show equal shares? Share your reasoning with the class.

Reveal the images one at a time and review children's responses. Have children support their conclusion for each shape. For shapes that show unequal shares, encourage children to describe how they would change or move the lines to show equal shares. They may draw on their MathBoards to do so. Encourage the other children to ask questions and critique each explanation.

Make Connections

Based on children's response to the Math Routine, choose one of the following:

1 Project the Interactive Reteach, Grade 1, Lesson 16.2.

2 Complete the Prerequisite Skills Activity:

Take a piece of paper and show it to the children. Fold it in half. Open it, and draw a line down the crease. Show the children the paper and ask: *Does this show equal or unequal shares?* Have children explain why they think the shares are equal or unequal. Now, fold the paper again with a line that does not make equal shares. Open it, trace the crease, and show it to the children. *Does this show equal or unequal shares?* Again, children should justify their choices. You may want to cut the pieces out so that children can lay them on top of one another and see that they are not the same size.

SHARPEN SKILLS

If time permits, use this on-level activity to build fluency and practice basic skills.

Fluency—Add within 10

Objective: Children practice adding within 10.

Materials: Addition Level 3 (Differentiated Instruction Blackline Masters)

Have children work in groups of three. The first child will say a number between 0 and 5. The second child will say a number between 0 and 5. The third child will then say the sum of the two numbers. The child who said the sum will then say the first addend for the next round. Children should continue as time allows, trying not to repeat any facts.

Children can then complete the Fluency Builder worksheet to practice addition within 10.

Small-Group Options

Use these teacher-guided activities with pulled small groups at the teacher table.

On Track

Materials: pattern blocks or plane shapes

Have children find two shapes that are equal in size and shape. Then have children combine the shapes and trace around the larger shape.

- How can you show half of the shape? Possible answer: I can draw a line to show 2 equal shares.

- How many halves are combined to make the shape? Possible answer: There are 2 halves that make the whole.

Have children repeat the activity by choosing different shapes.

Almost There (RtI)

Materials: Two-Dimensional Shapes (to combine) (Teacher Resource Masters), plane shapes, poster board

Use this Tabletop Flipchart Mini-Lesson to guide children in showing half of a shape.

Provide children with rectangles, squares, and circles and have them show equal shares that are halves. Children draw a line to show halves and shade half of the shape.

Tabletop Flipchart:
Lesson 16.3

Mini-Lesson

Ready for More

Materials: pieces of paper, markers

Have each child fold their paper in half, with the fold being the line that makes two equal shares. Then next to the fold, have children draw half of a shape. All of the children should pass their papers one person to the left. The person should open the paper and draw the other half of the shape on the other side of the fold. Challenge children to be creative with their shapes. When they are finished, have each open the paper and look at their drawing.

- How do you know that you each drew a half? Possible answer: There are 2 equal shares.

- How many halves make the whole shape? 2

Math Center Options

Use these student self-directed activities at centers or stations.   Key: ● Print Resources ● Online Resources

On Track

- ●● More Practice/Homework 16.3
- ● Fluency Builder: Addition Level 3
- ● Interactive Glossary: **halves**, **half of**

Almost There

- ● Reteach 16.3
- ● Interactive Reteach 16.3

Ready for More

- ● Challenge 16.3
- ● Interactive Challenge 16.3

ONLINE View data-driven grouping recommendations and assign differentiation resources.

During the *Spark Your Learning,* listen and watch for strategies students use. See samples of student work on this page.

Color Equal Shares Two Ways | Strategy 1

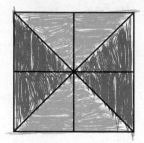 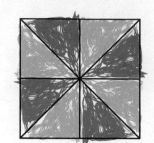

If children . . . color to show equal parts, they are demonstrating exemplary understanding of equal shares and making connections to what they have learned in the previous lesson.

Have these children . . . share how they know the shares are equal for two people. **Ask:**

Q How can you be sure that the number of shares are equal for two people?

Color Equal Shares the Same Way | Strategy 2

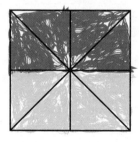 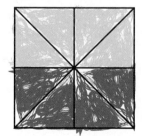

If children . . . simply reverse the colors, verify they understand there is another way to show halves.

Activate prior knowledge . . . by challenging them to use the smaller triangles or rectangles to make equal shares in a different way. **Ask:**

Q Is there another way to show two rectangles that are equal shares?

Q How can you show equal shares in a different way using the triangles?

COMMON ERROR: Color Unequal Shares

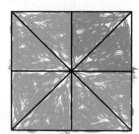 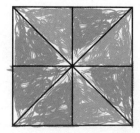

If children . . . color unequal shares, they may not understand the concept.

Then intervene . . . by having them outline rectangles that show equal shares before coloring. **Ask:**

Q What does it mean to have equal shares?

Q How can you change what you colored to make two equal shares?

Connect Concepts and Skills

Lesson **3**

Name _____

Partition Shapes into Halves

(I Can) identify and represent halves of circles and rectangles.

Spark Your Learning

How can you show equal shares for two people?

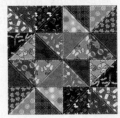

Check children's work.

PAIRS

Math Board

One way	Another way

Have children color the first square to show equal shares for two people.
Then color the second square to show a different way.

Module 16 • Lesson 3   four hundred sixty-seven **467**

---

① Spark Your Learning

▶ MOTIVATE

Ask children what they know about equal shares or equal parts. You may want to discuss what their understanding of sharing means.

EL   **CONNECT MATH IDEAS, REASONING, AND LANGUAGE** Compare and Connect

Remind children that shapes can be separated into equal shares or unequal shares. Have children describe in their own words different ways to show equal shares for two people. Have partners share their work and discuss how their work compares and contrasts.

▶ PERSEVERE

If children need support, guide them by asking:

Q **Assessing** How do you know if you show two equal shares? Possible answer: The same size part of the whole square will be colored in each color.

Q **Assessing • Use Tools** What is one way you can show equal shares for two people? I can color every other triangle different colors.

Q **Advancing** How will you know that your coloring shows the same amount of the shape for each person? Possible answer: I can count the triangles to make sure each person gets the same number.

Q **Advancing** What other shapes do you see that could show equal shares? Possible answer: I see that the four triangles on the left make a rectangle and the four triangles on the right make the same-size rectangle.

Turn and Talk How can you use the triangles to show equal shares of the whole square? Encourage children to describe the triangles they see within the triangle. Possible answer: The triangles are all the same size and shape. I can color the same number of triangles for each person.

▶ BUILD SHARED UNDERSTANDING

Select children who used various strategies and tools to share with the class how they solved the problem. Have children discuss why they chose a specific strategy or tool.

② Learn Together

Build Understanding

Task 1 (MP) **Use Structure** Read the problem aloud. Children may show their plate as a circle or rectangle. Suggest that drawing a line to show halves may help them to color half of the shape. Some children may wish to use paper shapes they can fold before drawing.

CONNECT TO VOCABULARY

Have children use their **Interactive Glossary** during this conversation to record their understanding.

 CONNECT MATH IDEAS, REASONING, AND LANGUAGE Compare and Connect

Before beginning the task, have children use their own words to define **halves**. Have partners discuss how their descriptions compare and contrast.

Sample Guided Discussion:

Ⓠ **How do you know that you are showing half of a plate?** Possible answer: Each part of the circle is the same size and shape.

 Turn and Talk Encourage children to share their work. Discuss how using two equal shares helps to identify halves. Possible answer: I made 2 equal shares. One of the shares is half of the circle.

Build Understanding

Carter wants half of his plate to have vegetables. How much of the plate is filled with vegetables?

A Draw to show the plate.

Color one of the halves to show the vegetables on the plate.

Possible answer:

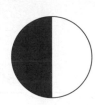

There are __2__ halves in __1__ whole.

B Show halves another way.

Possible answer:

 Turn and Talk How do you know that the part you colored is one of the halves? See possible answer at the left.

© Houghton Mifflin Harcourt Publishing Company • Image Credits: ©elmadesign/Shutterstock

LEVELED QUESTIONS

Depth of Knowledge (DOK)	Leveled Questions	What Does This Tell You?
Level 1 **Recall**	What do you call the two equal shares of a shape? halves	Children's answers will show that they know what halves are.
Level 2 **Basic Application of Skills & Concepts**	How can you make two halves in a circle? Possible answer: Draw 1 line through the center so that the 2 parts are the same size.	Children's answers will demonstrate that they understand how to make two halves.
Level 3 **Strategic Thinking & Complex Reasoning**	A line is drawn to make two unequal shares in the circle. Does this show halves of the circle? Why or why not? No. Halves have to be equal shares.	Children's answers will show an understanding of the connection between equal shares and halves.

Step It Out

1 Max wants to cut a board into halves.

A Draw the board as a rectangle.

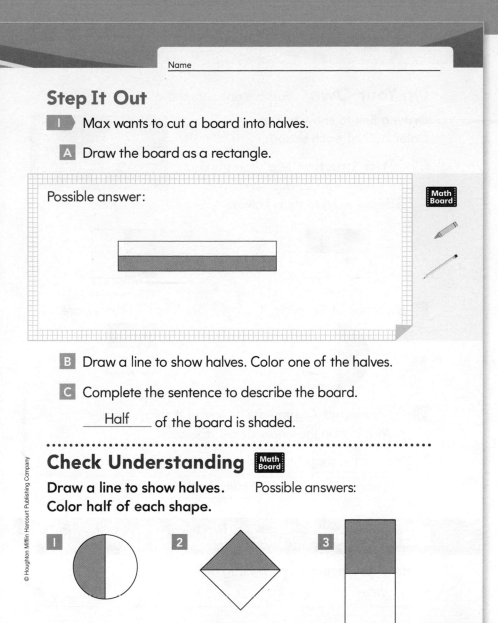

Possible answer:

B Draw a line to show halves. Color one of the halves.

C Complete the sentence to describe the board.

_____Half_____ of the board is shaded.

Check Understanding

Draw a line to show halves.
Color half of each shape.

Possible answers:

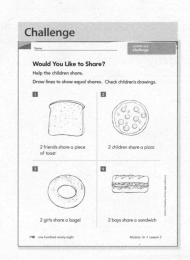

Module 16 • Lesson 3

four hundred sixty-nine **469**

Step It Out

Task 2 **MP** **Attend to Precision** Read the problem aloud. Review what halves are, and explain that each of the halves is *half* of the shape. Have children recall what they know about equal and unequal shares. Ask them to explain why it is important to be careful when drawing their picture to show halves.

EL **CONNECT MATH IDEAS, REASONING, AND LANGUAGE** **Compare and Connect**
Before beginning the task, have children use their own words to define *half* of a shape. Have partners share their work and discuss how their descriptions compare and contrast.

Sample Guided Discussion:

Q **How can you show halves of rectangles?** Possible answer: I can draw a line down the middle to show 2 equal shares.

Q **How much of the shape did you color?** Possible answer: half of the shape; I colored to show one of the halves.

Q **How many of the equal shares make the whole board?** The whole is two of the shares.

---

③ Check Understanding

Formative Assessment

Use formative assessment to determine if your students are successful with this lesson's learning objective.

Children who successfully complete the Check Understanding can continue to the On Your Own practice.

For children who miss 1 problem or more, work in a pulled small group with the Tabletop Flipchart Mini-Lesson.

ONLINE **Ed**

Assign the Digital Check Understanding to determine
• success with the learning objective
• items to review
• grouping and differentiation resources

④ Differentiation Options

Differentiate instruction for all children using small group mini-lessons and math center activities on page 467C.

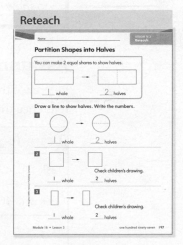

Lesson 16.3 **469**

On Your Own

- **Problem 4 • Use Structure** Children draw a line to show halves and color one half of the shape to solve a problem two different ways.

- **Problems 5–6** Children draw a line to show halves and then color half of the shape.

- **Problem 7 • Construct Arguments** Children write to justify why half of the shape is smaller than the whole shape.

⑤ Wrap-Up

Summarize learning with your class. Consider using the Exit Ticket, Put It in Writing, or I Can scale.

Exit Ticket

Draw a rectangle. Draw a line to make halves. Color half of the rectangle. Check children's work.

Put It in Writing

Explain how you know if a share of a shape is half of the shape.

I Can

The scale below can help you and your students understand their progress on a learning goal.

4	I can draw and explain why one of two equal shares of a shape is half of a shape.
3	I can identify and represent halves of circles and rectangles.
2	I can identify half of a circle or rectangle.
1	I can identify same-size shapes.

On Your Own   Possible answers shown.

Draw a line to show halves.
Color half of each shape.

4 **Use Structure** Mia shares half of her paper with Zara. Show two different ways to show halves.

5	Show half of the circle.	6	Show half of the square.

7 **Construct Arguments** Is half of a shape smaller or larger than the whole shape? Explain.

Half of the shape is smaller because 2 halves make the whole. Each part is smaller than the whole.

🎲 I'm in a **Learning Mindset!**

What helps me remember what to do?

_____

Learning Mindset

Try Again   Learns Effectively

Elicit from children that organizational tools, such as drawings and lists, may help them remember what to do when partitioning shapes into halves. *It is easier for me to remember what to do when I have a drawing or another type of visual model to remind me. How can you use a visual model to remember how to show different ways to show halves?*

Assignment Guide

Reference the chart below for problems associated with tasks. In a 2-day lesson, reference the chart to assign daily homework.

Learn Together Tasks	On Your Own Problems
Task 1, p. 468	Problem 4
Task 2, p. 469	Problems 5–6
Tasks 1–2, pp. 468–469	Problem 7

Partition Shapes into Halves

⊕ Use Structure Draw a line to show halves. Color half of each shape.

1 Rae sees a half moon in the sky. Show two different ways the moon could show halves.

    Possible answer shown.

2 Show half of the rectangle.

Possible answer shown.

3 Show half of the square.

Possible answer shown.

4 **Math on the Spot** Use the picture. Write numbers to solve.

The picture shows ___2___ halves.

The ___2___ equal shares make ___1___ whole.

Module 16 • Lesson 3   one hundred seventy-nine **P179**

ONLINE

Assign the Digital More Practice/ Homework for
• built-in student supports
• Actionable Item Reports
• Standards Analysis Reports

More Practice/Homework

Partition Shapes into Halves

Use More Practice/Homework pages to provide children with additional practice applying the concepts and skills presented in the lesson.

■ **Problem 1 • STEM** Patterns of the moon can be observed and described. Children depict a half moon two different ways by drawing a line and coloring one half of the circle.

■ **Problems 1–3 • Use Structure** Children show halves of each shape by drawing a line. Then they color one half of the shape.

Math on the Spot

Encourage children to complete Problem 4 and then review their work with a family member or a friend by watching the *Math on the Spot* video.

Assignment Guide

Reference the chart below for problems associated with tasks. In a 2-day lesson, reference the chart to assign daily homework.

Learn Together Tasks	More Practice/Homework Problems
Task 1, p. 468	Problem 1
Task 2, p. 469	Problems 2–3
Tasks 1–2, pp. 468–469	Problems 4–6

Test Prep

The Test Prep items provided assess understanding of halves.

Additional Test Prep opportunities are available online and in *Getting Ready for High Stakes Assessment.*

Spiral Review

The spiral review problems will help determine if children have retained information taught in the past. Here, children will need to demonstrate an ability to use a picture graph to answer questions. **(8.1)**

Test Prep

Fill in the bubble next to the correct answer.

5 Which shape shows halves?

  ●   ○

6 Which shows half of a square?

○   ○   ●

Spiral Review

Some children were asked which shape they like best.

Shapes We Like						
▲ triangle	▲	▲	▲	▲	▲	
● circle	●	●	●			
■ square	■	■				

Use the picture graph to answer the questions.

7 How many children chose ▲? ___5___ children

8 How many more children chose ● than ■? ___I___ more

16.4 Partition Shapes into Fourths

LESSON FOCUS AND COHERENCE

■ Major ☐ Supporting ○ Additional

Mathematics Standards

○ Partition circles and rectangles into two and four equal shares, describe the shares using the words *halves, fourths,* and *quarters,* and use the phrases *half of, fourth of,* and *quarter of.* Describe the whole as two of, or four of the shares. Understand for these examples that decomposing into more equal shares creates smaller shares.

Mathematical Practices and Processes

- Use appropriate tools strategically.
- Look for and make use of structure.

I Can Objective

I can identify and represent fourths of circles and rectangles.

Learning Objectives

Separate circles and rectangles into fourths and describe the whole as four of the shares.

Language Objectives

- Explain how many fourths are in a whole.
- Explain the meaning of *fourths, fourth of, quarters,* and *quarter of.*

Vocabulary

New: fourth of, fourths, quarter of, quarters

Lesson Materials: MathBoard, crayons, pencils, scissors, Squares, Circles, and Rectangles (Teacher Resource Masters)

Mathematical Progressions

Prior Learning	Current Development	Future Connections
Children: - identified circles, squares, and rectangles. **(GrK, 16.1, 16.2, 16.4)** - composed simple shapes. **(GrK, 16.6)**	**Children:** - partition circles and rectangles into four equal shares. - identify four equal shares as quarters or fourths. - understand that a fourth of (quarter of) a shape is smaller than the whole shape.	**Children:** - will identify, describe, and draw two, three, or four equal shares. **(Gr2, 22.2–22.3)** - will identify these equal shares as halves, thirds, and fourths (quarters). **(Gr2, 22.2–22.3)** - will use different ways to show halves, thirds, and fourths (quarters). **(Gr2, 22.5)**

PROFESSIONAL LEARNING

Using Mathematical Practices and Processes

Use appropriate tools strategically.

The concept of fourths is abstract, but children develop the conceptual understanding by using concrete and visual models as tools for showing fourths. Manipulatives can be used as tools, with which children can show fourths by putting four of the same shape together to make another shape. Drawings, or visual models, are also used to represent fourths. Children draw lines to make four equal shares and shade a fourth of the shape. By using these representations as tools, children can visualize what a fourth is and how it is made. They recognize key features that make a share a quarter and can apply this knowledge when trying to explain why another model, concrete or visual, shows fourths or does not show fourths.

ACTIVATE PRIOR KNOWLEDGE • Halves

Use these activities to quickly assess and activate prior knowledge as needed.

Math Routine

True or False? Does the image show halves? If you think the image shows halves, say *true*. If you think the image does not show halves, say *false*.

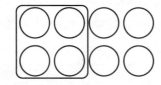

Reveal one image at a time. Ask how many children say *true*, that is, the shape does show halves. Invite children to share their reasoning. Recognize other children who may disagree and have them refute the claim that the shape shows halves.

After children have argued both sides, move to the next image and proceed in the same way.

Make Connections

Based on children's response to the Math Routine, choose one of the following:

1 Project the Interactive Reteach, Grade 1, Lesson 16.3.

2 Complete the Prerequisite Skills Activity:

Hold up a sheet of paper. Fold the paper in half. Point to each of the sides of the fold. **Ask:** *What do we call these shares?* Children could identify these shares as halves. When asked to justify their answer, they could say that each of the equal shares is half of the paper. Shade one of the equal shares. **Ask:** *How much of the shape is shaded?* Children could say that half of the shape is shaded.

If children continue to struggle, use Tier 2 Skill 25.

SHARPEN SKILLS

If time permits, use this on-level activity to build fluency and practice basic skills.

Fluency—Subtraction Within 10

Objective: Children demonstrate an ability to subtract fluently within 10.
Materials: 10 craft sticks, Fluency Builder: Subtraction Level 4 (Differentiated Instruction Blackline Masters)

Place a pile of ten craft sticks in the center of the table. Have one child take some of the sticks in the pile. Have another child write an equation to model the craft sticks being taken away. Have children repeat the activity with children changing roles.

Children can then complete the Fluency Builder worksheet to practice subtraction within 10.

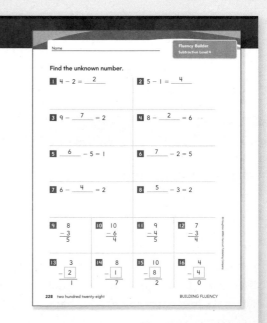

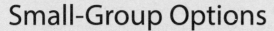

Small-Group Options

Use these teacher-guided activities with pulled small groups at the teacher table.

On Track

Materials: pattern blocks (squares), MathBoard

Have children put four squares together as fourths to make a whole.

- How can you be sure that the shares are equal? Possible answer: They are the same size.

- What do you call one of the squares? Possible answer: a fourth or quarter of the large square

Next, have each child draw a square and then draw lines to make four equal shares. Children should compare their results to other members in the group.

- How many quarters make the shapes? 4

- How can you know that each of your drawings shows fourths? Possible answer: There are 4 equal shares.

Almost There   Rtl

Materials: construction paper, Equal and Unequal Shares Cards (Teacher Resource Masters), poster board

Use this Tabletop Flipchart Mini-Lesson to guide children in showing fourths.

Provide children with rectangles, squares, and circles and have them show equal shares that are fourths. Children draw a line to show fourths or quarters and shade a quarter or a fourth of the shape.

Tabletop Flipchart: Lesson 16.4

Mini-Lesson

Ready for More

Materials: MathBoard

A pizza is cut into equal slices. Four friends want to share the pizza. Each friend will get an equal share. Draw a visual model of this problem. Color one person's share.

- How do you describe the part that each person gets? fourth or quarter

- How do you know that the shares are equal? They are the same size.

Math Center Options

Use these student self-directed activities at centers or stations.   **Key:** ● **Print Resources** ● **Online Resources**

On Track

- ●● More Practice/Homework 16.4
- ● Fluency Builder: Subtraction Level 4
- ● Interactive Glossary: **fourths, fourth of, quarter, quarter of**
- ● My Learning Summary
- ●● Standards Practice: Partition Shapes Into Equal Shares, and Describe the Shares

Almost There

- ● Reteach 16.4
- ● Interactive Reteach 16.4
- ●● Rtl Tier 2 Skill 25: Identify Halves

Ready for More

- ● Challenge 16.4
- ● Interactive Challenge 16.4

 ONLINE Ed   View data-driven grouping recommendations and assign differentiation resources.

During the *Spark Your Learning*, listen and watch for strategies students use. See samples of student work on this page.

Show Four Equal Shares in Both Shapes — Strategy 1

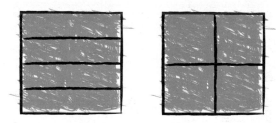

If children . . . correctly draw lines to make four equal shares, they are demonstrating exemplary understanding of equal shares and making connections to what they learned in previous lessons.

Have these children . . . share how they know the shares are equal. **Ask:**

Q How can you be sure that the shares are equal?

Show Four Equal Shares in Different Ways — Strategy 2

If children . . . use the same shape to show four equal shares in different ways, they demonstrate understanding of equal shares.

Activate prior knowledge . . . by encouraging them to use a different shape to show four equal shares. **Ask:**

Q How can you use a circle to show four equal shares?

COMMON ERROR: Draw 4 Lines in the Shape

If children . . . draw four lines, they may be confusing showing four equal shares with drawing four lines.

Then intervene . . . by having them count the number of shares. **Ask:**

Q How many shares are there when you draw four lines inside the shape?

Q How can you be sure that the shares you show are equal shares?

Connect Concepts and Skills

Lesson 4

Name _____

Partition Shapes Into Fourths

(I Can) identify and represent fourths of circles and rectangles.

Spark Your Learning

How do you show 4 equal shares?

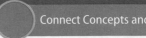 PAIRS

 Scissors

 Math Board

 Pencil / Marker

Check children's work.

Provide children with a paper circle and rectangle or have them cut out a paper circle and rectangle. Children fold the shapes to show 4 equal shares. Children then draw to show how they folded the shapes.

Module 16 • Lesson 4   four hundred seventy-one   **471**

① Spark Your Learning

▶ MOTIVATE

Provide pairs of children with a paper circle and rectangle. Squares, Rectangles, and Circles are in the Teacher Resource Masters for children to cut out.

EL **CONNECT MATH IDEAS, REASONING, AND LANGUAGE** Compare and Connect

Remind children they have previously shown both equal and unequal shares in shapes. Before starting the task, you may want to have children describe in their own words how to show equal shares. Have partners share their work and discuss how their work compares and contrasts.

▶ PERSEVERE

If children need support, guide them by asking:

Q **Assessing** How will you show four equal shares? Possible answer: I will fold each shape to show 4 parts that are the same size and shape.

Q **Advancing** How can showing two halves help you show four equal shares? Possible answer: I can show halves by folding the shape once. Then I can fold the shape again to show 4 equal shares.

Q **Advancing • Use Tools** What could you do to be sure the 4 shares are equal? Possible answer: I could cut along the fold lines to make 4 pieces and check that they are all the same size.

Turn and Talk What steps did you take to show four equal shares? Encourage children to share their work. Ask them to compare the methods for finding four equal shares of a circle and four equal shares of a square. Possible answer: First, I fold the paper circle in half. Then I keep it folded and fold it in half again. When I open it up, it shows four equal shares.

▶ BUILD SHARED UNDERSTANDING

Select children who used various strategies and tools to share with the class how they solved the problem. Have children discuss why they chose a specific strategy or tool.

② Learn Together

Build Understanding

Task 1 (MP) **Use Tools** Read the problem aloud. Color is used as a tool to visually highlight a fourth of the shape.

CONNECT TO VOCABULARY

Have children use their **Interactive Glossary** during this conversation to record their understanding.

(EL) **CONNECT MATH IDEAS, REASONING, AND LANGUAGE** Compare and Connect

Before beginning the task, have children use their own words to define **fourths** and **fourth of**. Have partners share their work and discuss how their descriptions compare and contrast.

Sample Guided Discussion:

Q **How can you make four equal shares?** Possible answer: I can draw a line that makes halves out of each half.

Q **How could you show fourths another way in the rectangle?** Possible answer: I could show 2 triangles in each smaller square.

 Turn and Talk Encourage children to share their work. Discuss how the shares must be equal, and since there are four, each is one fourth. Possible answer: There are 4 equal-sized parts.

Build Understanding

Harper paints shapes to show fourths.
She draws a line to show halves.
How can she show fourths?

A Show fourths. Color a fourth of the shape.

Possible answers:

There are ___4___ fourths in ___1___ whole.

B Show another way to make fourths. Color a fourth of the shape.

Possible answer:

Connect to Vocabulary

fourths: four equal shares of a whole

fourth of: Each part is a fourth of the whole.

 **Turn and Talk** How do you know that the part you colored is one fourth of the shape? See possible answer at the left.

© Houghton Mifflin Harcourt Publishing Company • Image Credits: ©sunspire/Adobe Stock

---

LEVELED QUESTIONS

Depth of Knowledge (DOK)	Leveled Questions	What Does This Tell You?
Level 1 **Recall**	What do you call the four equal shares of a shape? fourths or quarters	Children's answers will show that they know what fourths are.
Level 2 **Basic Application of Skills & Concepts**	How can you make four fourths in a shape? Possible answer: Draw 2 lines to make 4 parts that are the same size.	Children's answers will demonstrate that they understand how to make fourths.
Level 3 **Strategic Thinking & Complex Reasoning**	Four unequal shares make a shape. Are the shares fourths? Explain. No. Fourths have to be equal shares.	Children's answers will show an understanding of the connection between equal shares and fourths.

Step It Out

I Ben made a rectangle volleyball court in the sand. Then he separated the rectangle into four quarters.

A Draw the volleyball court.

B Draw lines to show four quarters.

C Color a fourth of the court blue.

D Color a quarter of the court green.

> **Connect to Vocabulary**
>
> **quarter** or **quarter of:** another way to name a fourth, or a fourth of

Possible answer:

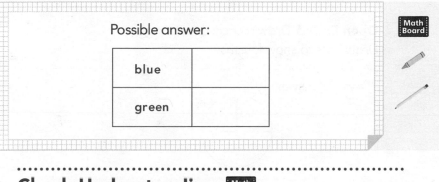

Math Board

....

Check Understanding [Math Board]

Draw lines to show fourths.
Color one quarter of the shape.

Possible answers:

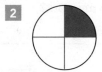
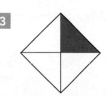

1 2 3

© Houghton Mifflin Harcourt Publishing Company

Step It Out

Task 2 **(MP) Use Structure** Read the problem aloud. Children show 4 equal shares of a rectangle, applying what they know about fourths to understand quarters.

CONNECT TO VOCABULARY

Have children use their **Interactive Glossary** during this conversation to record their understanding.

(EL) CONNECT MATH IDEAS, REASONING, AND LANGUAGE Compare and Connect

Have children describe how many of the shares make the whole rectangle volleyball court. Encourage them to use new vocabulary from the lesson. Discuss how their descriptions compare and contrast.

Sample Guided Discussion:

Q Is the shape you colored blue the same size as the shape you colored green? Explain. Possible answer: Yes, each fourth, or quarter, is an equal share of the rectangle. Equal shares are the same size.

Q Is a fourth, or quarter, of a shape larger or smaller than the whole shape? smaller Is a fourth, or quarter, of a shape larger or smaller than a half of that shape? Explain. Possible answer: A half is one of two equal shares of a whole shape. A fourth is one of four equal shares of the shape, so a fourth is smaller than a half.

data checkpoint

③ Check Understanding

Formative Assessment

Use formative assessment to determine if your students are successful with this lesson's learning objective.

Children who successfully complete the Check Understanding can continue to the On Your Own practice.

For children who miss 1 problem or more, work in a pulled small group with the Tabletop Flipchart Mini-Lesson.

ONLINE [Ed] **Assign the Digital Check Understanding to determine**
- success with the learning objective
- items to review
- grouping and differentiation resources

④ Differentiation Options

Differentiate instruction for all children using small group mini-lessons and math center activities on page 471C.

Reteach

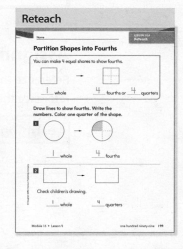

Challenge

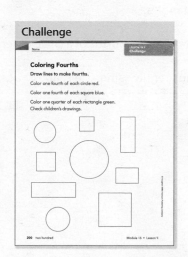

Assign the Digital On Your Own for
- built-in student supports
- Actionable Item Reports
- Standards Analysis Reports

On Your Own

- **Problem 4 • Health and Fitness** Choosing a variety of foods supports healthy growth and development. Each meal should contain at least one fruit or vegetable. Whole grain breads are a healthy choice. Children show a way to cut a square sandwich into fourths.

- **Problem 5 • Open Ended** Children choose whether to draw a circle, square, or nonsquare rectangle, and then draw lines to show fourths.

(5) Wrap-Up

Summarize learning with your class. Consider using the Exit Ticket, Put It in Writing, or I Can scale.

Exit Ticket

Draw a square. Draw lines to make quarters. Color one quarter of the square.

Check children's answers.

Put It in Writing

Explain how you know if a share of a shape is a quarter of the shape.

I Can

The scale below can help you and your students understand their progress on a learning goal.

4	I can draw and explain why one of the four equal shares of a shape is a fourth of a shape.
3	I can identify and represent fourths of circles and rectangles.
2	I can identify fourths of a circle or rectangle.
1	I can identify same-size shapes.

On Your Own

4 (MP) **Attend to Precision** Frank cuts his square sandwich into fourths. Show one way Frank can cut his sandwich.

Possible answer:

5 **Open Ended** Draw a circle or rectangle. Draw lines to show fourths.

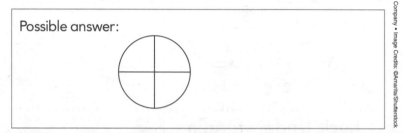

Possible answer:

🔆 I'm in a **Learning Mindset!**

What helped me finish my work?

_____

_____

Learning Mindset

Try Again   Learns Effectively

Remind children about the importance of organizing their work so they are able to complete it. Using visual models can help children see ways to make fourths. *In what ways does using visual models help you to learn about fourths? Seeing your finished visual models helps you understand when your work is complete.*

Assignment Guide

Reference the chart below for problems associated with tasks. In a 2-day lesson, reference the chart to assign daily homework.

Learn Together Tasks	On Your Own Problems
Tasks 1–2, pp. 472–473	Problems 4–5

Name _____

LESSON 16.4
More Practice/
Homework

ONLINE
Video Tutorials and
Interactive Examples

Partition Shapes into Fourths

(MP) **Attend to Precision** Draw lines to show fourths. Color one quarter of the shape.

1 Possible answer:

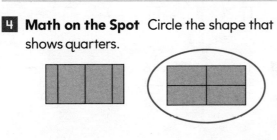

2 Possible answer:

3 Possible answer:

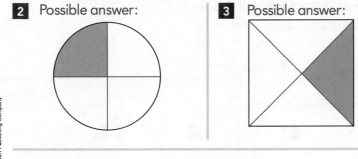

4 **Math on the Spot** Circle the shape that shows quarters.

© Houghton Mifflin Harcourt Publishing Company

ONLINE
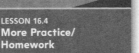

Assign the Digital More Practice/
Homework for
• built-in student supports
• Actionable Item Reports
• Standards Analysis Reports

More Practice/Homework

Partition Shapes into Fourths

Use More Practice/Homework pages to provide children with additional practice applying the concepts and skills presented in the lesson.

■ **Problems 1–3 • Attend to Precision** Children show fourths by drawing lines to show four equal shares and coloring one quarter of the shape.

Math on the Spot

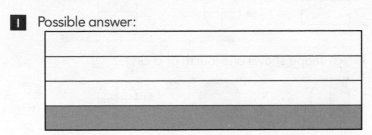

Encourage children to complete Problem 4 and then review their work with a family member or a friend by watching the *Math on the Spot* video.

Assignment Guide

Reference the chart below for problems associated with tasks. In a 2-day lesson, reference the chart to assign daily homework.

Learn Together Tasks	More Practice/Homework Problems
Task 1, p. 472	Problems 1–3
Tasks 1–2, pp. 472–473	Problems 4–6

Lesson 16.4   **474A**

Test Prep

The Test Prep items provided assess understanding of identifying fourths or quarters of a circle or rectangle.

Additional Test Prep opportunities are available online and in *Getting Ready for High Stakes Assessment*.

Spiral Review

The spiral review problems will help determine if children have retained information taught in the past. Here, children will need to demonstrate an ability to draw a line to show 2 shapes the same size and shape that can make the square. Children also demonstrate an ability to add and subtract within 20. **(16.1 and 13.5)**

Test Prep

Fill in the bubble next to the correct answer.

5 Which shape shows quarters?

○   ●   ○

6 Which shape shows one fourth of a circle?

○   ○   ●

Spiral Review

7 Draw a line to show 2 shapes that are the same size.

Possible answer:

Add or subtract.

8 $\begin{array}{r} 9 \\ +6 \\ \hline 15 \end{array}$	**9** $\begin{array}{r} 7 \\ +4 \\ \hline 11 \end{array}$	**10** $\begin{array}{r} 5 \\ +7 \\ \hline 12 \end{array}$	**11** $\begin{array}{r} 8 \\ +9 \\ \hline 17 \end{array}$
12 $\begin{array}{r} 18 \\ -9 \\ \hline 9 \end{array}$	**13** $\begin{array}{r} 14 \\ -6 \\ \hline 8 \end{array}$	**14** $\begin{array}{r} 16 \\ -7 \\ \hline 9 \end{array}$	**15** $\begin{array}{r} 13 \\ -7 \\ \hline 6 \end{array}$

Name _____

Vocabulary

1 Write a vocabulary word to describe.

Vocabulary

halves
fourths
quarters

halves

fourths or quarters

Concepts and Skills

Fill in the bubble next to the correct answer.

2 Brooke uses 2 shapes that are the same size to make a square. Which is her shape?

3 Which circle shows 4 shapes that are the same size and shape?

4 Which shows half of the rectangle?

Module 16   four hundred seventy-five **475**

ONLINE

Assign the Digital Module Review for
- built-in student supports
- Actionable Item Reports
- Standards Analysis Reports

MODULE
16

REVIEW

Module Review

Use the Module Review as practice and review of the module's content.

Vocabulary

Have children review the terms for this module. Encourage children to think about the meaning of each term in their own words before completing Problem 1.

Concepts and Skills

(MP) **Use Tools** Prior to assigning the Module Review, help children list the strategies or tools used throughout the module. As each is listed, guide children how they might use each strategy or tool to solve a problem.

As children start the review, read Item 2. Remind children of the list of tools used in the module. Ask them to think of a strategy or a tool that could be used to solve the problem.

After children have completed the review, discuss Item 2 and ask a child to show his or her solution with the strategy or tool used. Have children who used a different tool share their solutions.

DATA-DRIVEN INSTRUCTION

Before moving on to the Module Test, use the Module Review results to intervene based on the table below.

MTSS (RtI)

Items	Lesson	DOK	Content Focus	Intervention
2	16.1	3	Identify a square made from two same-size shapes.	Reteach 16.1
3	16.1	2	Identify a circle made from four same-size shapes.	Reteach 16.1
4	16.3	2	Identify a shape that shows halves.	Reteach 16.3

Module Review continued

Possible Scoring Guide

Items	Points	Description
1	1	writes the correct term for one visual model
1	2	writes the correct term for both visual models
2	2	identifies the correct shape
3	2	identifies the correct shape
4	2	identifies the correct shape
5	2	identifies the correct shape
6	2	identifies the correct shape
7	2	identifies the correct shape
8	1	answers one or two parts correctly
8	2	answers all parts correctly
Totals point possible = 16 points		

The Unit 5 Performance Task in the Assessment Guide assesses content from Modules 14–16.

Fill in the bubble next to the correct answer.

5 Which shape shows halves?

6 Which shape shows 4 quarters?

7 Which shape shows unequal shares?

8 Does the shape show equal shares?
Fill in the bubble to answer.

	Yes	No
	●	○
	●	○
	○	●

DATA-DRIVEN INSTRUCTION

Before moving on to the Module Test, use the Module Review results to intervene based on the table below.

MTSS (RtI)

Items	Lesson	DOK	Content Focus	Intervention
5	16.3	2	Identify a shape that shows halves.	Reteach 16.3
6	16.4	2	Identify a shape that shows quarters.	Reteach 16.4
7	16.2	2	Identify a shape that shows unequal shares.	Reteach 16.2
8	16.2	2	Identify a shape that shows equal shares.	Reteach 16.2

Module Test

The Module Test is available in alternative versions in your Assessment Guide. The print versions are available in your Assessment Guide.

 data checkpoint

ONLINE

 Ed

Assign the Digital Module Test to power actionable reports including
- proficiency by standards
- item analysis

MODULE
16

TEST

Form A

Name _____

Module 16 • Form A
Module Test

1 James cuts his cracker in half. Which picture shows his cracker?

2 Which shows half of the circle?

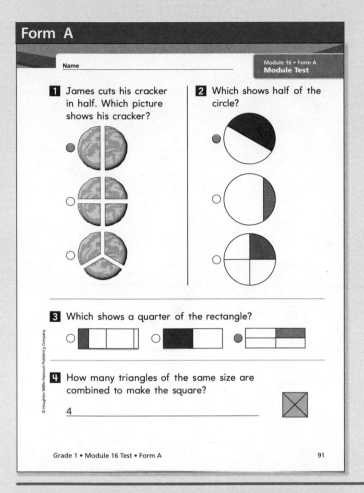

3 Which shows a quarter of the rectangle?

4 How many triangles of the same size are combined to make the square?

4

Grade 1 • Module 16 Test • Form A   91

Form A

Module 16 • Form A
Module Test   Name _____

5 Pieces that are the same size and shape as the triangle are combined to make the square. How many pieces are used?

2 _____

6 Circle the shapes that show equal shares. Put a box around the shapes that show unequal shares. You will use all the shapes.

7 Circle the shapes that show halves. Put a box around the shapes that show fourths. You will use all the shapes.

92

Form B

Name _____

Module 16 • Form B
Module Test

1 Beth cuts her pizza in half. Which picture shows Beth's pizza?

2 Which shows a quarter of the circle?

3 Which shows half of the rectangle?

4 How many squares of the same size are combined to make the rectangle?

4

Grade 1 • Module 16 Test • Form B   93

Form B

Module 16 • Form B
Module Test   Name _____

5 Pieces that are the same size and shape as the small rectangle are combined to make the large rectangle. How many pieces are used?

2 _____

6 Circle the shapes that show equal shares. Put a box around the shapes that show unequal shares. You will use all the shapes.

7 Circle the shapes that show halves. Put a box around the shapes that show fourths. You will use all the shapes.

94

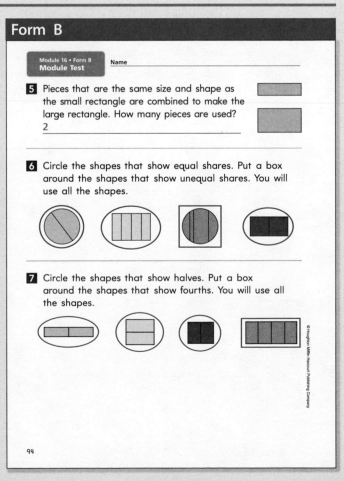

Module 16   476A